CATS

EASY PIANO SELECTION

MUSIC BY

ANDREW LLOYD WEBBER
BASED ON 'OLD POSSUM'S BOOK OF PRACTICAL CATS' BY
T.S.ELIOT

FABER MUSIC LTD
3 QUEEN SQUARE   LONDON WC1

CHAPPELL INTERNATIONAL MUSIC PUBLISHERS LTD

250 591 612

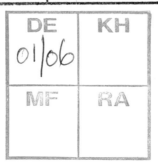
Also available:
Cats, the Book of the Musical; Ten Songs from Cats;
Cats Piano/Vocal Album; Memory; Memory for Easy Piano.

Cats is recorded on a Polydor double record album (CATX 001)

CONTENTS

Jellicle Songs for Jellicle Cats

Text by
TREVOR NUNN
and RICHARD STILGOE after T.S.ELIOT

Music by
ANDREW LLOYD WEBBER

With expression

mf

Are you blind when you're born?__ Can you see in the dark?__ Can you look at a King?__ Would you sit on his throne?__Can you say of your bite __ that it's worse than your bark?__Are you cock of the walk __ when you're walk-ing a-lone?__ Be-cause

Rhythmically

Jel-li-cles are and Jel-li-cles do, Jel-li-cles do and Jel-li-cles

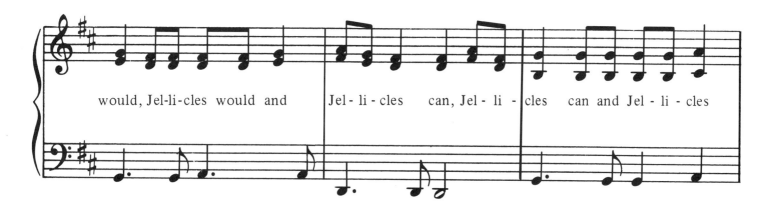

would, Jel-li-cles would and Jel-li-cles can, Jel-li-cles can and Jel-li-cles

Slower

do. When you fall on your head,_ do you

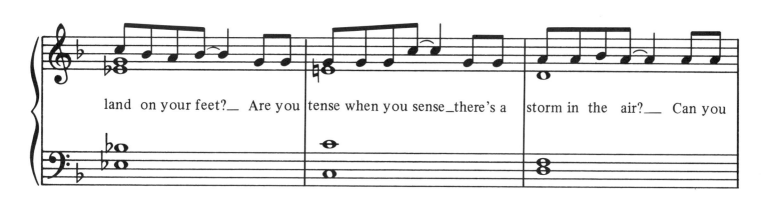

land on your feet?_ Are you tense when you sense_there's a storm in the air?_ Can you

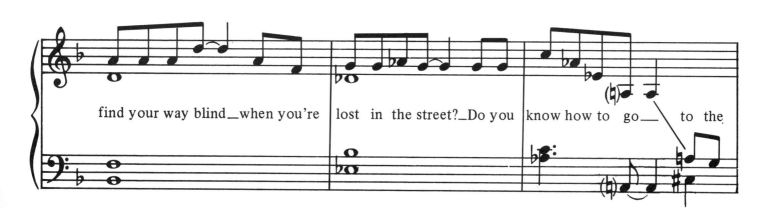

find your way blind_when you're lost in the street?_Do you know how to go_ to the

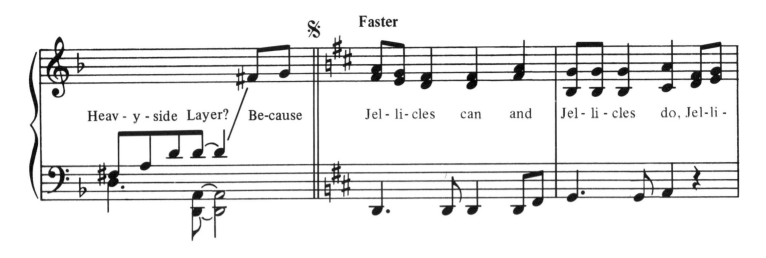

Heav-y-side Layer? Be-cause Jel-li-cles can and Jel-li-cles do, Jel-li-

cles do and Jel-li-cles can, Jel-li-cles can and Jel-li-cles do, Jel-li-

To Coda ⊕ **Slowly, reverent**

cles can and Jel-li-cles do. The

mys-ti-cal di-vin-i-ty of un-a-shamed fe-

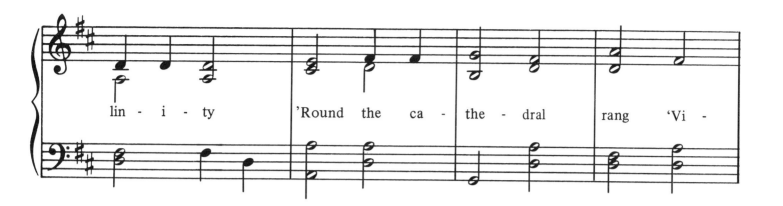

lin - i - ty 'Round the ca - the - dral rang 'Vi -

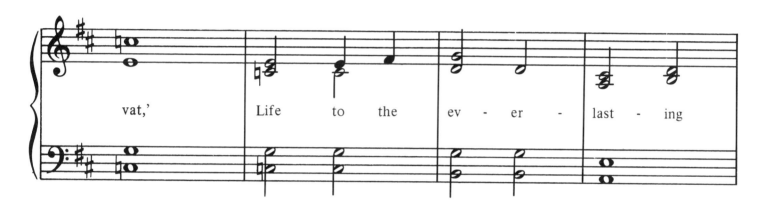

vat,' Life to the ev - er - last - ing

cat! Fe - line, fear - less, faith - ful and true To

D.S. al Coda

CODA

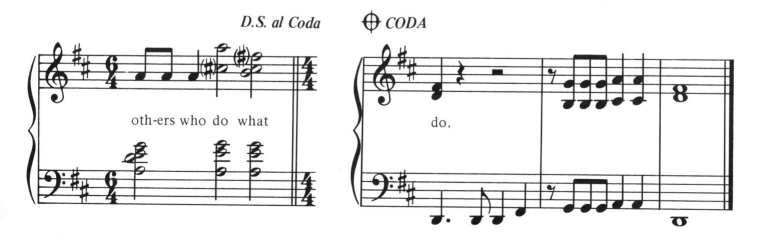

oth-ers who do what do.

The Old Gumbie Cat

Text by
T.S. ELIOT

Music by
ANDREW LLOYD WEBBER

cat. That's what makes a gum - bie cat. But when the day's hus-tle and

bus - tle is done, Then the Gum - bie Cat's work is but hard - ly be - gun. And

when all the fam - i - ly's in bed and a - sleep She tucks up her skirts to the

base - ment to creep. She is deep-ly con-cerned with the ways of the mice: Their be -

ha-viour's not good and their man-ners not nice; So when she has got them lined

up - on the mat - ting, She teach-es them mu-sic, cro - chet-ing and tat - ting.

Very Slowly

ritard. I have a Gum-bie Cat in mind, her

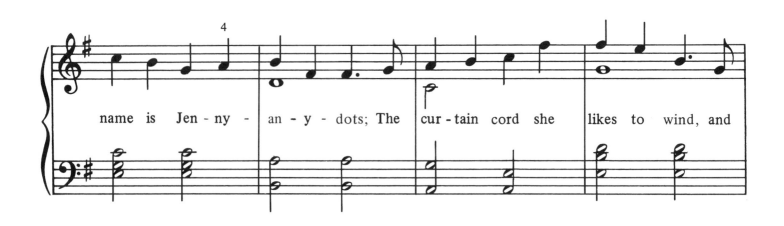

name is Jen - ny - an - y - dots; The cur - tain cord she likes to wind, and

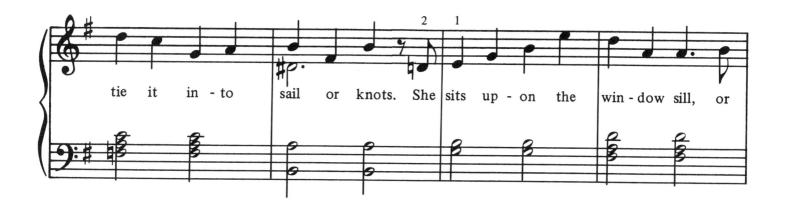

tie it in - to sail or knots. She sits up - on the win - dow sill, or

an - y - thing that's smooth and flat: She sits and sits and sits and sits, and

that's what makes a Gum - bie Cat, that's what makes a __ Gum - bie __ Cat.

ritard.

Bustopher Jones:
The Cat about Town

Text by
T.S.ELIOT

Music by
ANDREW LLOYD WEBBER

Dignified

Bus - to-pher Jones__ is not skin and bones,__ In fact he's re - mark-ab - ly fat. He does - n't haunt pubs,__ he has eight or nine clubs,__ For he's the St. Jame-s's Street Cat! He's the cat we all greet__ as we walk down the street__ In his coat of fas - tid - i - ous black: No

com - mon place mou-sers have such well cut trou-sers Or such an im-pec-a-ble

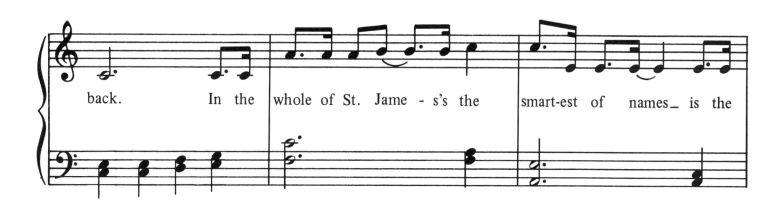

back. In the whole of St. Jame - s's the smart-est of names__ is the

name of the Brum-mel of cats; And we're all of us proud __ to be

nod-ded and bowed __ to By Bus - to - pher Jones in white spats!

Slightly Slower

My vis - its are oc-cas-ion-al to the

Sen -ior Ed - u - cat-ion-al, And it is a - gainst the rules For

a - ny one cat to be - long both to that and the Joint Su - pe - ri - or

Schools. When I'm seen in a hur-ry there's prob-ab- ly cur-ry At the

Si - a - mese or at the Glut-ton; — If I look full of gloom then I've

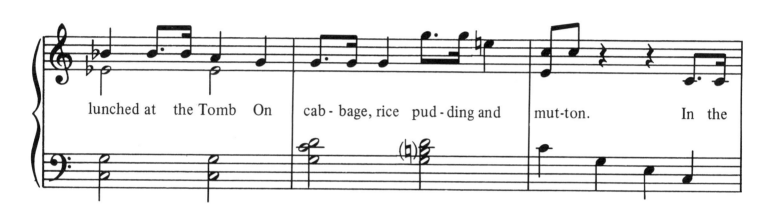

lunched at the Tomb On cab - bage, rice pud - ding and mut-ton. In the

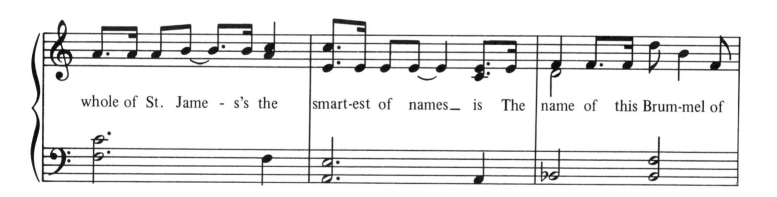

whole of St. Jame - s's the smart-est of names— is The name of this Brum-mel of

cats; And we're all of us proud— to be nod- ded or bowed— to By

Bus - to-pher Jones in white, Bus - to-pher Jones in white, Bus - to-pher Jones in white

spats! He's a twen-ty-five pound-er, or I am a boun-der, And he's

put-ting on weight ev-'ry day: But I'm so well pre-served _ be-

cause I've ob-served _ All my life a rou-tine, and I'd say, I am

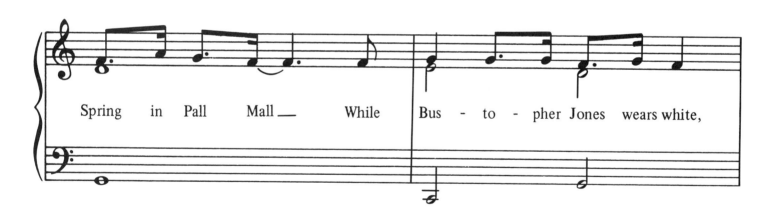

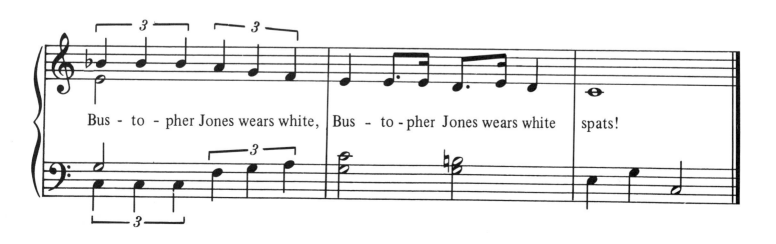

still in my prime I shall last out my time. That's the

word from this stout-est of cats. It must and it shall — be

Spring in Pall Mall — While Bus - to - pher Jones wears white,

Bus - to - pher Jones wears white, Bus - to - pher Jones wears white spats!

Old Deuteronomy

Text by
T.S.ELIOT

Music by
ANDREW LLOYD WEBBER

Moderately Slow

Old Deu-ter'-on-o-my's lived a long time; He's a cat who has lived man-y lives in suc-ces-sion. He was fa-mous in pro-verb and fa-mous in rhyme, a long while be-fore Queen Vic-to-ria's ac-ces-sion.

Old Deu - ter - on - o - my's bur - ied nine wives and

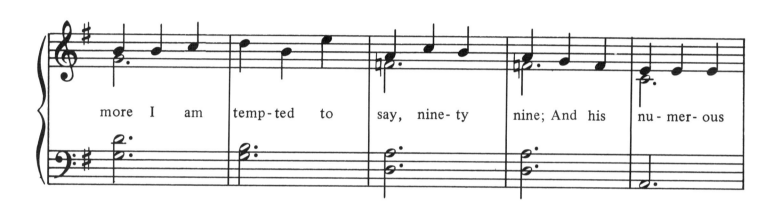

more I am temp - ted to say, nine - ty nine; And his nu - mer - ous

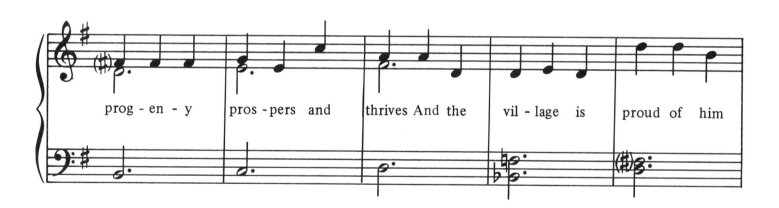

prog - en - y pros - pers and thrives And the vil - lage is proud of him

in his de - cline. At the sight of that plac - id and

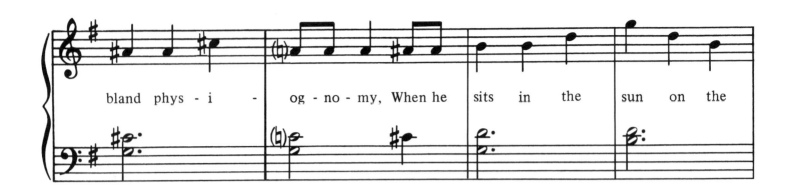

bland phys - i - og - no - my, When he sits in the sun on the

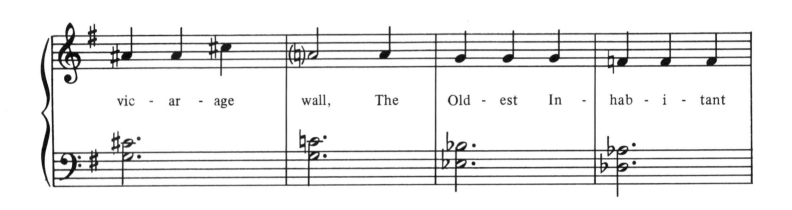

vic - ar - age wall, The Old - est In - hab - i - tant

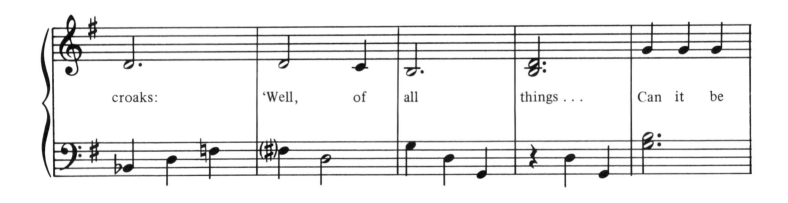

croaks: 'Well, of all things . . . Can it be

real - ly? . . . Yes! No! Ho! Hi! Oh, my eye!_____ My

mind may be wan-der-ing, but I con-fess, I be-lieve it is

Old Deu-ter - on-o-my.' 'Well, of all things . . .

Can it be real - ly? . . . Yes! No! Ho! Hi! Oh, my eye!_____

_ My mind may be wan-der-ing, but I con - fess, I be-

lieve it is Old Deu - ter - on - o - my!'   'Well, of all

things . . .   Can it be real - ly? . . .   Yes! No! Ho! Hi! Oh, my

eye! _____   My legs may be tot - ter - y,   I must go

slow And be care - ful of Old Deu - ter - on - o - my.'

Gus: The Theatre Cat

Text by
T.S.ELIOT

Music by
ANDREW LLOYD WEBBER

Gus is the Cat at the The - a - tre Door. His name, as I
coat's ver - y shab by, he's thin as a rake, And he suf - fers from

ought to have told you be - fore, Is real - ly As - par - a - gus but
pal - sy that makes his paw shake. Yet he was, in his youth, quite the

that's such a fuss To pro - nounce, that we u - sual - ly call him just
smart - est of cats: But no lon - ger a ter - ror to mice and to

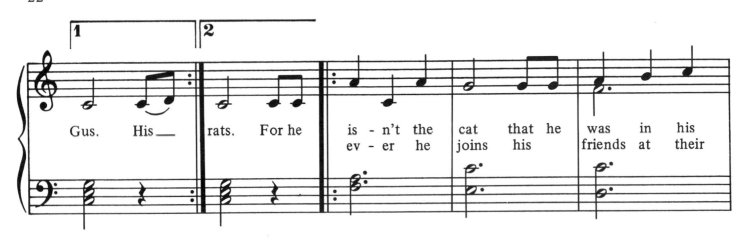

Gus. His — rats. For he
is-n't the cat that he was in his
ev-er he joins his friends at their

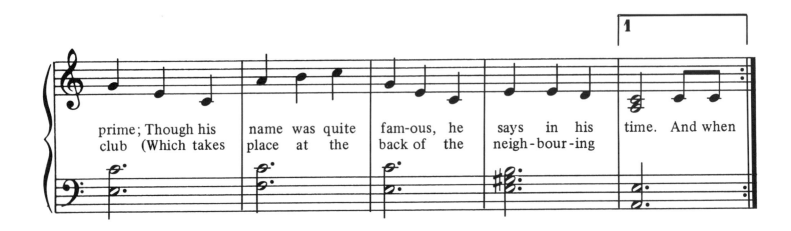

prime; Though his name was quite fam-ous, he says in his time. And when
club (Which takes place at the back of the neigh-bour-ing

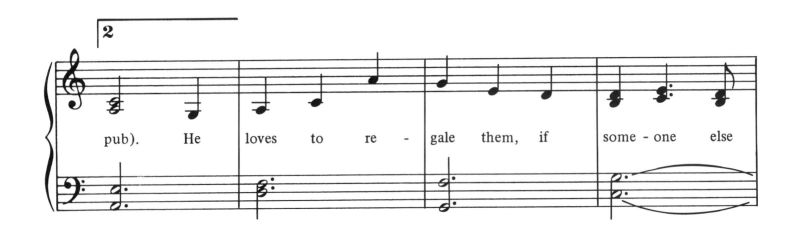

pub). He loves to re-gale them, if some-one else

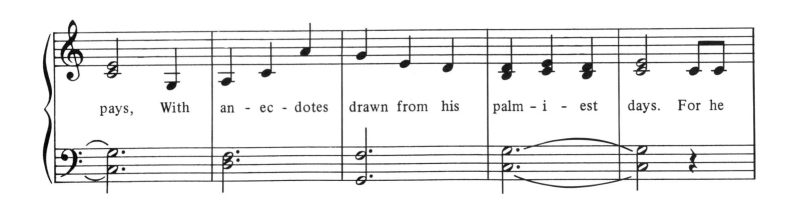

pays, With an-ec-dotes drawn from his palm-i-est days. For he

once was a star of the high-est de - gree: He has act - ed with
likes to re - late his suc - cess on the Halls, Where the Gal -ler - y

Irv - ing, he's act - ed with Tree. And he
once gave him sev - en cat calls. But his grand-est cre - a - tion, as

he loves to tell, Was Fire-fro - re - fid - dle the Fiend of the
rit.

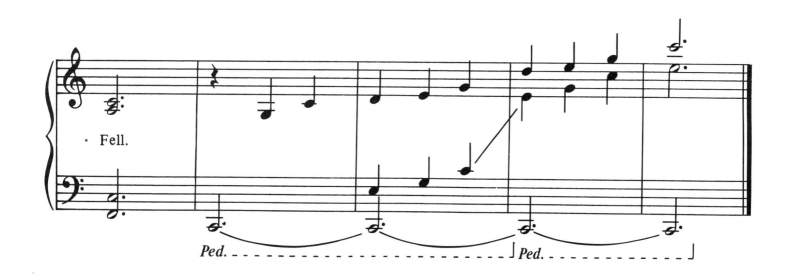

· Fell.

Ped. - - - - - - - - - - - - - - - *Ped.*

Skimbleshanks: The Railway Cat

Text by
T.S.ELIOT

Music by
ANDREW LLOYD WEBBER

Lively

whis - per down the line at e - lev - en thir - ty - nine When the

Night Mail's read - y to de - part, Say - ing,

'Skim-ble, where is Skim-ble, has he gone to hunt the thim-ble? We must

find him or the train can't start.' All the

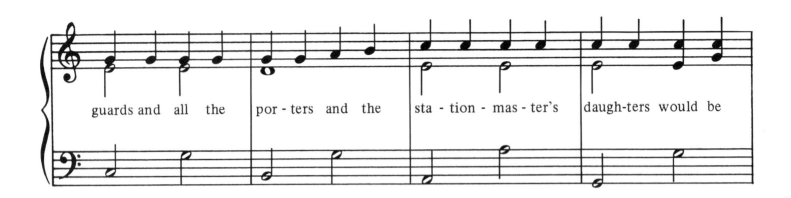

guards and all the por - ters and the sta - tion - mas - ter's daugh-ters would be

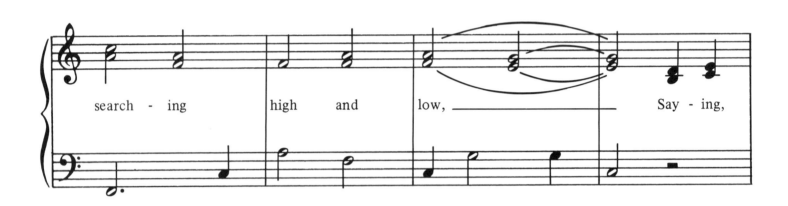

search - ing high and low, _____ Say - ing,

'Skim-ble where is Skim-ble, for un - less he's ver - y nim - ble Then the

Night Mail just can't go.' 'At e -

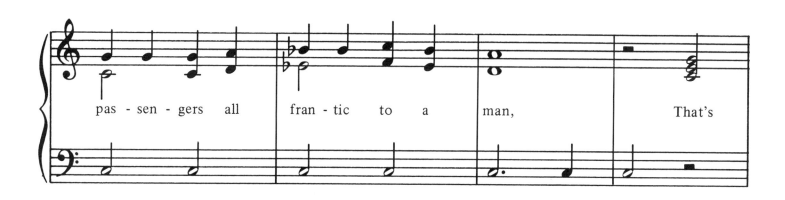

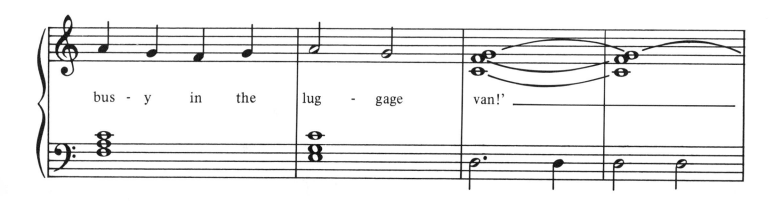

Then he gave one flash of his

glass - green eyes And the sig - nal went 'All

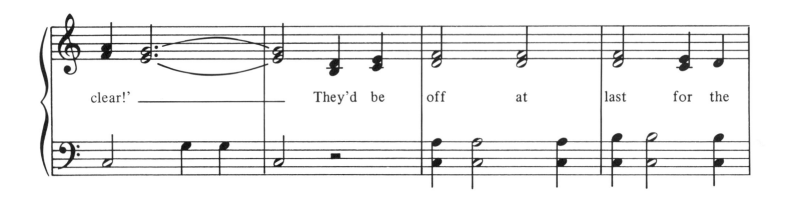

clear!' _____ They'd be off at last for the

north - ern part of the North - ern Hem - i -

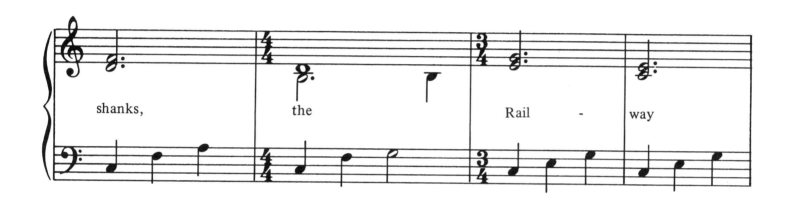

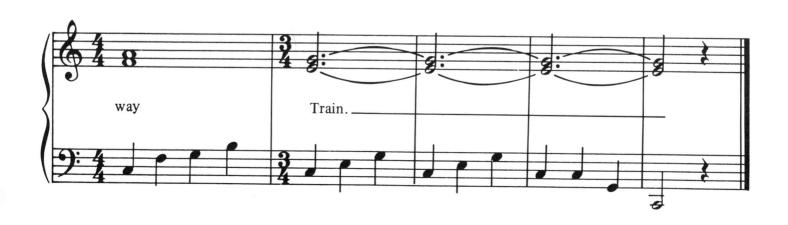

Mr Mistoffelees

Text by
T.S.ELIOT

Music by
ANDREW LLOYD WEBBER

Freely

The | great-est ma - gi - cians have | some-thing to learn | from Mis-ter Mis - tof-fe-lees

f

Rhythmically

Con-jur-ing Turn, — | And we all say, | Oh, well I

continue pedal

nev - er! Was there ev - er a | cat so cle-ver as | Mag - i - cal

Mis - ter - Mis - tof - fe - lees! | He is | qui-et, he is small, he is

black from his ears to the tip of his tail;— He can creep thro' one ti-ni-est

crack, He can walk on the nar-row-est_ rail. He can pick an-y card from a

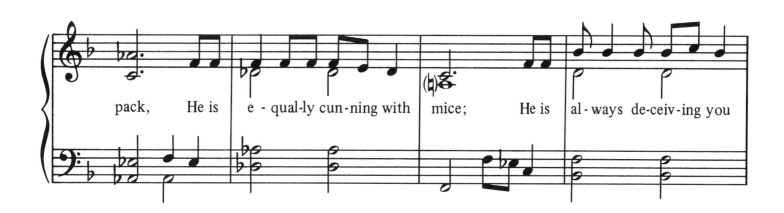

pack, He is e-qual-ly cun-ning with mice; He is al-ways de-ceiv-ing you

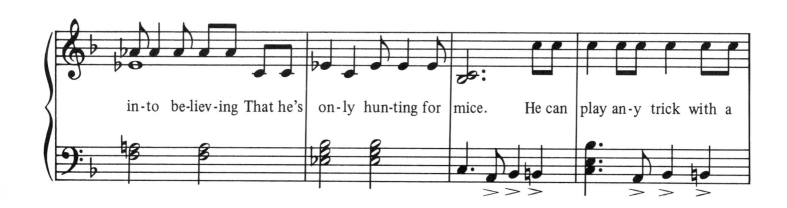

in-to be-liev-ing That he's on-ly hun-ting for mice. He can play an-y trick with a

cork   Or a spoon and a bit of fish paste;   If you look for a knife   or a

Freely

fork   And you think it is mere-ly mis - placed,   You have seen it one mo-ment, and

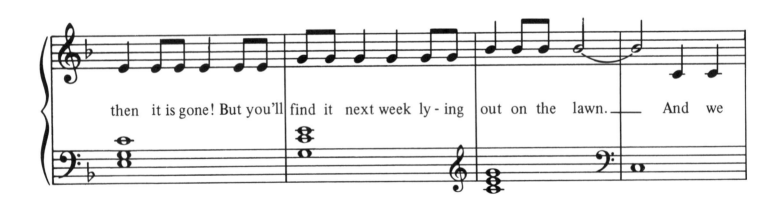

then   it is gone! But you'll find it   next week ly - ing   out on the   lawn.___   And we

Rhythmically

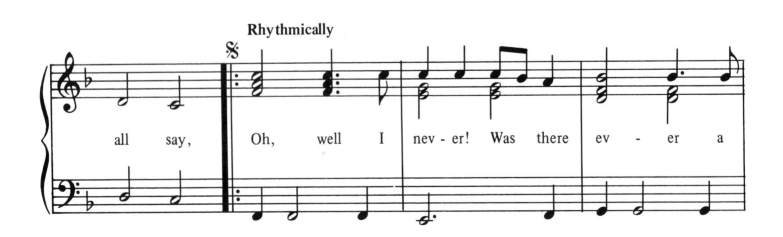

all   say,   Oh,   well   I   nev - er! Was there   ev - er   a

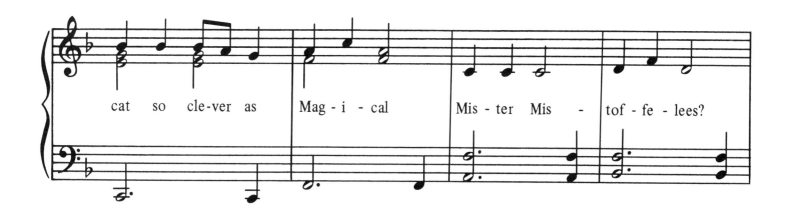

cat so cle-ver as Mag - i - cal Mis - ter Mis - tof - fe - lees?

To Coda ⊕ **Freely**

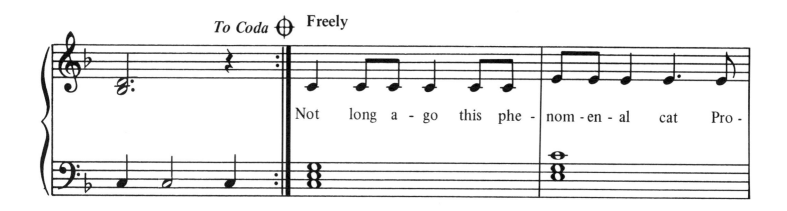

Not long a - go this phe - nom - en - al cat Pro -

D.S. al Coda
with Repeat

duced sev - en kit-tens right out of a hat! ___ And we all said:

⊕ **CODA**

Memory

Text by
TREVOR NUNN
after T.S.ELIOT

Music by
ANDREW LLOYD WEBBER

Freely

Let the mem - 'ry _____ live a - gain.

Ev - 'ry street lamp seems _____ to beat _____ a
Burnt out ends of smok - y days _____ the

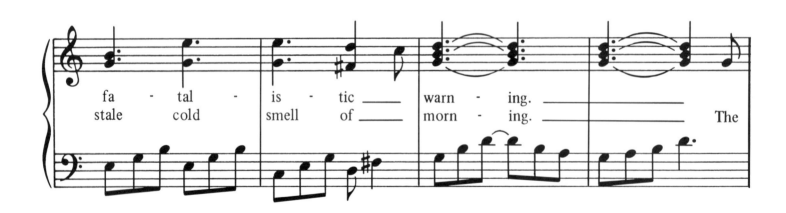

fa - tal - is - tic _____ warn - ing. _____
stale cold smell of _____ morn - ing. _____ The

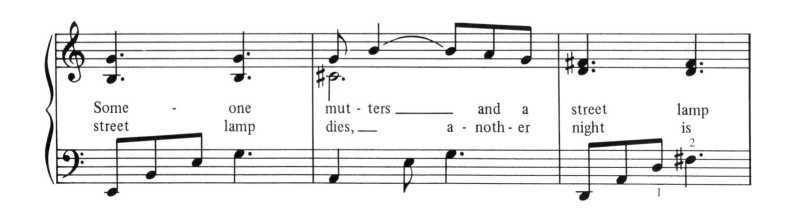

Some - one mut - ters _____ and a street lamp
street lamp dies, _____ a - noth - er night is

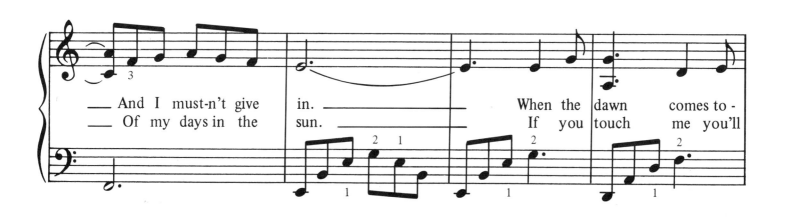

To Coda ⊕

night will be a mem-o - ry too _____ And a new day _____
un - der-stand what hap-pi-ness is. _____ Look a new day _____

_____ will be - gin.

D.S. al Coda   ⊕ CODA

_____ has be -

gun.

The Ad-dressing of Cats

Text by
T.S.ELIOT

Music by
ANDREW LLOYD WEBBER

Moderately Slow

mf

with pedal

You've heard of sev-eral kinds of cat, And my o-pin-ion now is that You should need no — in-ter-pret-er To un-der-stand our char-ac-ter. You've learned e-nough to take the view That cats are much like me and you. You've seen us both_at_ work and games, And learnt a-bout_our_

pro - per names, Our   ha - bits and __ our __   hab - i - tat: But   How would you ad-

dress   a   cat?   So   first   your mem-o-

ry   I'll   jog   And __ say: a   cat   is   not   a

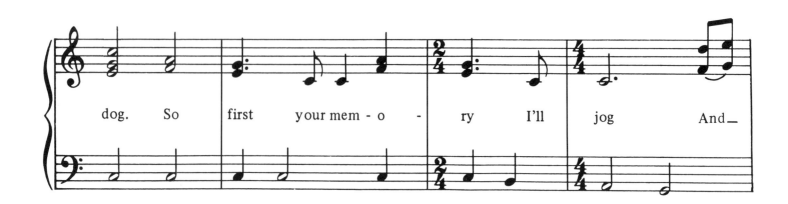

dog. So   first   your mem-o-   ry   I'll   jog   And__

say: a cat is not a dog. With

cats, some say, one rule is true: Don't speak 'till

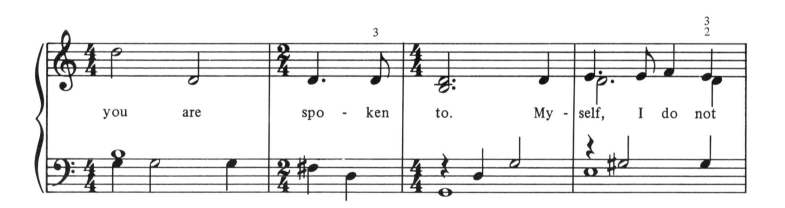

you are spo - ken to. My - self, I do not

hold with that. I say, you should ad - dress a cat. But al - ways keep in

42

mind that he re - sents fa - mil - i - ar - i - ty. You bow, and

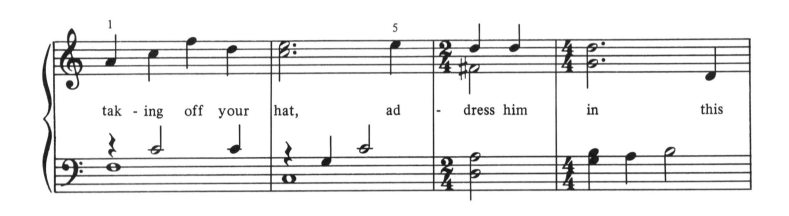

tak - ing off your hat, ad - dress him in this

form: 'Oh, cat!' Be - fore a cat will con - de-scend To

molto ritard   *a tempo*

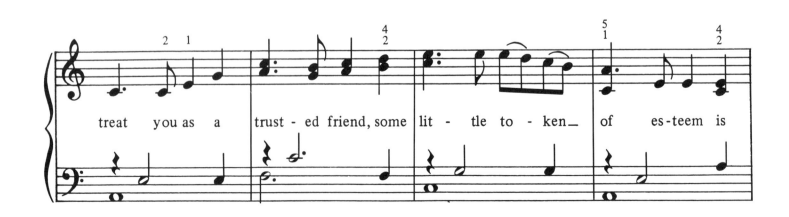

treat you as a trust - ed friend, some lit - tle to - ken of es-teem is

need - ed like a dish of cream; And you might now and

then sup-ply Some cav - i - are or Strass - burg Pie, Some

pot - ted grouse_ or __ sal - mon paste: He's sure to have__ his __

per - son-al taste. And so in time_ you_ reach your aim, And call him

by his name.   A   cat's en - ti - tled

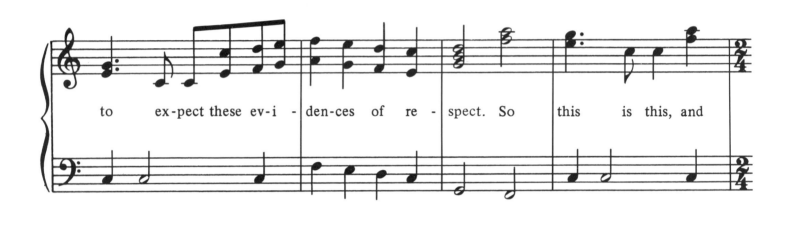

to   ex-pect these ev-i - den-ces of re - spect. So   this   is this, and

that   is   that: And   there's how you ad - dress   a

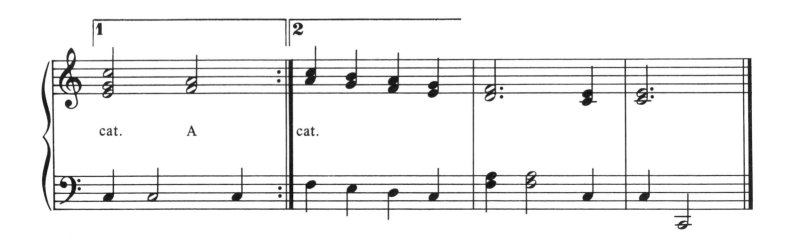

cat.   A   cat.

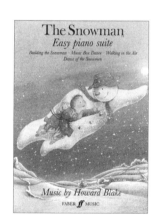

PIANO

Cats (easy piano selection) *Andrew Lloyd Webber*

ISBN 0-571-50831-6

Children's Album *arranged by Daniel Scott*

ISBN 0-571-51103-1

The Faber Book of Showstoppers *arranged by Alan Gout*

ISBN 0-571-51063-9

The Faber Book of TV Themes *arranged by Alan Gout*

ISBN 0-571-51753-6

Great Film and TV Themes *Carl Davis*

ISBN 0-571-51740-4

It's never too late to play piano (repertoire) *Pamela Wedgwood*

ISBN 0-571-51836-2

Jane Austen's World *arranged by Richard Harris*

ISBN 0-571-51793-5

Shakespeare's World *arranged by Richard Harris*

ISBN 0-571-51907-5

The Snowman (easy piano suite) *Howard Blake*

ISBN 0-571-58044-0

Educational publications from Faber Music

PIANO

Up-Grade! Piano Grades 0-1 *Pamela Wedgwood*

ISBN 0-571-51737-4

More Up-Grade! Piano Grades 0-1 *Pamela Wedgwood*

ISBN 0-571-51956-3

Up-Grade! Piano Grades 1-2 *Pamela Wedgwood*

ISBN 0-571-51560-6

Up-Grade! Piano Grades 2-3 *Pamela Wedgwood*

ISBN 0-571-51561-4

Up-Grade! Piano Grades 3-4 *Pamela Wedgwood*

ISBN 0-571-51775-7

Up-Grade! Piano Grades 4-5 *Pamela Wedgwood*

ISBN 0-571-51776-5

The Jazz Piano Master *John Kember*

ISBN 0-571-51791-9

Progressive Jazz Studies. Level 1 *John Kember*

ISBN 0-571-51582-7

Progressive Jazz Studies. Level 2 *John Kember*

ISBN 0-571-51583-5

FABER *ff* MUSIC